~ MY ~
BABY
RECORD BOOK

Featuring traditional nursery rhymes

Published by Hinkler Books Pty Ltd
45–55 Fairchild Street
Heatherton Victoria 3202 Australia
www.hinkler.com.au

hinkler

Author: Kate Cody
Cover design: Hinkler Studio

ISBN: 978 1 7436 7869 5

Printed and bound in China

Welcome to the World

Our country's leader

...... Justin Trudeau ....

News headlines

....

....

....

....

Cost of a loaf of bread

...... $2.29 ....

Cost of a stamp

...... $0.70 ....

Cost of a newspaper

...... $1.75 ....

Memorable moments

....

....

....

....

....

Birth announcement card

Higgledy piggledy my little hen,
She lays eggs for gentlemen.
Sometimes nine and sometimes ten,
Higgledy piggledy my little hen.

Naming Your Baby Boy

Baby boy's name

....

....

Reason for choosing name

....

....

Other names considered

....

....

....

....

Nicknames

....

....

Naming Ceremony

Date

....

Place

....

Baby boy's outfit

....

....

Godparents

....

....

....

Naming day photo

8

Description of naming ceremony
and celebration

Cards and presents

How baby behaved

....

....

....

....

....

....

Who was there

....

....

....

....

....

....

....

....

....

....

....

....

....

....

Two little dickey-birds

sitting on a wall,

One named Peter,

One named Paul.

Fly away Peter,

Fly away Paul.

Come back Peter!

Come back Paul!

9

Baby Boy's Family Tree

Baby Boy's Family

Mother's birth date
October 12th 1989

Father's birth date
December 10th 1982

Mother's place of birth
Richmond BC

Father's place of birth
Vancouver, BC

Mother's life story in a nutshell

Father's life story in a nutshell

Significant family dates

Brothers and sisters

Ages of brothers and sisters

10

great grandmother	great grandfather	great grandmother	great grandfather	great grandmother	great grandfather	great grandmother	great grandfather
Irene Musto	Dave Musto	Nicky Myrna	Bob Bill				

grandmother	grandfather	grandmother	grandfather
Susan	Chris	Victoria	John

mother
Carly Nicole

father
Christopher Edward

baby
Christian John

Sleepy Nights

Description of baby's nursery

Jungle theme for
Christians room.

Description of the cot/crib

White Crib

First slept in cot/crib

First slept in own room

First slept through the night

Memorable moments

*L*ittle Boy Blue

Come blow your horn,

The sheep's in the meadow

The cow's in the corn.

Where is the boy

Who looks after the sheep?

He's under the haystack

Fast asleep!

Helping Your Baby Boy to Sleep

Going to bed routine at night

....

....

....

Lullabies that baby loves

....

....

....

Bedtime stories that baby loves

....

....

Bedtime toys or comforters

....

....

Settling techniques tried

....

Baby asleep

Most successful settling technique

....

....

....

....

....

Food to Grow

Food and Drink Firsts

First began eating puréed food

....

....

First began eating mashed food

....

....

First began eating solid food

....

....

Foods that baby loves

....

First drank from a spout cup

....

First drank through a straw

....

First drank from a cup

....

First sat in a high chair

....

....

First ate with a spoon

....

....

First began sharing the family meal

....

Known food sensitivities

....

....

....

Memorable moments

....

....

....

....

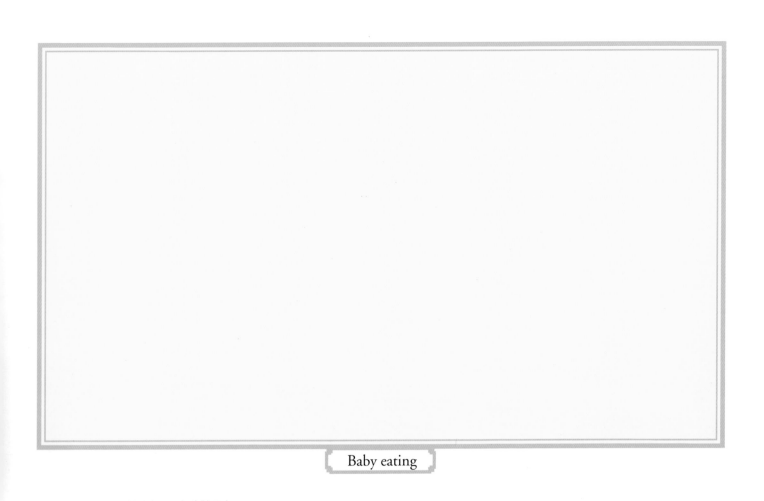

Baby eating

Pat-a-cake, pat-a-cake, baker's man,

Bake me a cake as fast as you can.

Pat it and prick it and mark it with B,

And put it in the oven for baby and me.

15

Developmental Milestones

Began following with eyes

....

....

Began turning head to sound

....

....

First smiled

July 2016 (less than a
month old)

Began grasping rattle or soft toy

....

....

Began putting rattle or toy to mouth

....

....

First cooed

August 2016

....

First held up head

....

....

First rolled over

....

....

Growing baby

Began to sit alone

....

....

First crawled

....

....

First stood with support

....

....

Began to walk with support

....

....

Started babbling

....

....

First words

....

....

Started taking steps

....

....

Walked alone

....

....

First tooth

....

....

Sally go round the sun,
Sally go round the moon,
Sally go round the chimney pots,
On a Sunday afternoon.

Things Baby Loves

Comforter

....

....

....

....

Soft toys

....

....

....

....

Toys

....

Things around home

....

....

....

....

Books

....

....

....

....

Nursery rhymes

....

....

....

....

Lullabies

....

....

....

....

Animals or pets

....

....

....

....

Games

....

....

....

....

Activities

....

....

....

....

....

....

People

....

....

....

....

....

Places

....

....

....

....

....

This is the way the ladies ride,
Nimble, nimble, nimble, nimble;
This is the way the gentlemen ride,
A gallop, a trot, a gallop, a trot;
This is the way the farmers ride,
Jiggety-jog, jiggety-jog;
This is the way the farmboys ride,
Hobbledy-hoy, hobbledy-hoy;
This is the way the huntsmen ride,
A gallop, a gallop,
And down in the ditch!

19

Fun with Water

Bath time

First bath

....

First time in a big bath

....

....

Began sharing a bath

....

....

....

Bath toys

....

....

....

Bath games

....

....

....

Water Play

First trip to the beach or lake

....

First water play in garden

....

....

*R*ub-a-dub dub,
Three men in a tub,
And who do you think they be?
A butcher, a baker,
A candle-stick maker,
Turn them out,
Knaves all three!

First splash in paddling pool

....

First dip in swimming pool

August 2016 in Papas
pool

First swimming class

....

....

....

....

Your baby boy's swimming costume

....

....

....

....

....

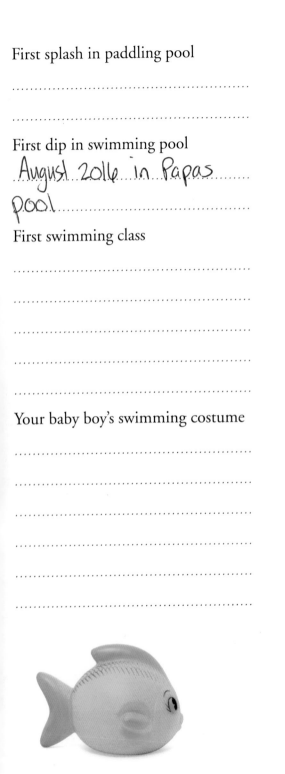

*Y*ou shall have a fishy
On a little dishy,
You shall have a fishy
When the boat comes in.

Baby in the bath

Going Out

First playgroup

....

....

....

First time baby fed the ducks

....

....

First visit to the playground

....

....

....

First time on a merry-go-round

....

....

....

First visit to the zoo

August 2016 with
brother Erik.
Calgary Alberta

....

Family weekend activities

....

....

Going Out to:

The swimming pool

....

....

....

Cafes and restaurants

....

....

....

The shops

....

....

....

Parks and gardens

....

....

....

The beach

....

....

....

The countryside

....

....

....

22

Bus

....
....
....
....

Train

....

Plane

....

Other

....
....

Visiting

Grandparents

August 2016 ....

....

Relatives

....
....

Friends

....
....

Trips by:

Pram/stroller

....
....
....
....

Car

....
....

Clever Boy

First waved goodbye

....
....

First played peek-a-boo

....
....

First clapped hands

....
....

First pulled a pull-along toy

....
....

First picked up tiny objects

....
....

First stacked blocks

....
....

First turned the pages of a book

....
....

First joined in singing a song

....
....

First put on their own clothes

....
....

First danced

....
....

Other baby firsts

....
....
....
....
....
....
....
....

*O*ne, two,

Buckle my shoe.

Three, four,

Knock on the door.

Five, six,

Pick up sticks.

Seven, eight,

Lay them straight.

Nine, ten,

Big fat hen!

Clever baby boy

*R*ound and round the garden,

Like a teddy bear.

One step, two steps,

Tickle you under there!

Healthy Boy

Vaccinations

Age	Vaccinations	Date Given*
Birth	Hepatitis B	
2 months	Diptheria/Tetanus/Pertussis Oral Polio Vaccine Hepatitis B H. Influenzae Type b	
4 months	Diptheria/Tetanus/Pertussis Oral Polio Vaccine Hepatitis B H. Influenzae Type b	
6 months	Diptheria/Tetanus/Pertussis Oral Polio Vaccine	
12 months	Measles/Mumps/Rubella Hepatitis B H. Influenzae Type b	

Note – vaccination schedules may vary. The above is a guide only.

Other Vaccinations

Age	Vaccinations	Date Given

Any reactions

Health and Development Checks

Health care professionals

....

....

....

....

....

Visits to health care professionals

Age	Date	Comment

Three cheeky monkeys,

Bouncing on the bed,

One fell off and bumped his head.

Mama called the doctor,

And the doctor said;

No more monkeys,

Bouncing on the bed!

27

2 Months Old

Usually woke for the day at

....

....

Went to bed for the day at

....

....

Daytime sleep routine

....

....

....

....

Daytime feeding routine

....

....

....

Night-time sleeping
and feeding routine

....

....

....

Weight

....

Length

....

Head circumference

....

Crying periods

....

....

....

Best way to calm your baby boy

....

....

....

....

Changes

....

....

....

New sounds

....

....

....

....

New firsts

....

....

....

....

Your baby boy's temperament

....

....

....

....

Nicknames

....

....

....

Description of a typical day

....

....

....

....

....

Baby at 2 months

Photo caption

....

....

....

Date photo taken

....

....

4 Months Old

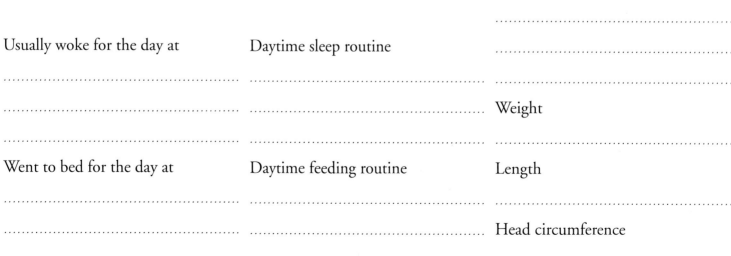

Baby at 4 months

Photo caption

....

....

....

Date photo taken

....

Night-time sleeping
and feeding routine

....

....

....

Weight

....

Length

....

Head circumference

....

Usually woke for the day at

....

....

....

Went to bed for the day at

....

....

Daytime sleep routine

....

....

....

Daytime feeding routine

....

....

Time spent playing on the floor

....

....

....

....

Crying periods

....

....

Best way to calm your baby boy

....

....

....

....

Changes

....

....

....

New sounds

....

....

....

New firsts

....

....

....

....

Your baby boy's temperament

....

....

Nicknames

....

....

....

....

Description of a typical day

....

....

....

Preferred activities

....

....

....

Preferred foods

....

....

....

....

....

....

....

....

6 Months Old

Usually woke for the day at

....

Went to bed for the day at

....

....

Daytime sleep routine

....

....

Daytime feeding routine

....

....

Night-time sleeping
and feeding routine

....

....

....

....

Weight

....

Length

....

Head circumference

....

Time spent playing on the floor

....

....

Crying periods

....

....

....

Best way to calm your baby boy

....

....

....

Changes

....

....

....

New teeth

....

....

Teething symptoms and remedies

....

....

....

Baby at 6 months

New sounds

....

....

New firsts

....

....

....

Your baby boy's temperament

....

....

....

Nicknames

....

....

Description of a typical day

....

....

Preferred activities

....

....

....

Photo caption

....

....

....

Date photo taken

....

Preferred foods

....

....

....

33

8 Months Old

Usually woke for the day at

....

....

Went to bed for the day at

....

....

Daytime sleep routine

....

....

Daytime feeding routine

....

....

Night-time sleeping
and feeding routine

....

....

....

Photo caption

....

....

....

....

Date photo taken

....

Baby at 8 months

Weight

....

Length

....

Head circumference

....

Time spent playing on the floor

....

....

Crying periods

....

....

Best way to calm your baby boy

....

....

....

Changes

....

....

....

New teeth

....

....

....

Teething symptoms and remedies

....

....

....

New sounds

....

New firsts

....

....

Your baby boy's temperament

....

....

Nicknames

....

....

Description of a typical day

....

....

....

....

Preferred activities

....

....

....

Preferred foods

....

....

35

10 Months Old

Usually woke for the day at

....

Went to bed for the day at

....

....

Daytime sleep routine

....

....

Daytime feeding routine

....

....

Night-time sleeping
and feeding routine

....

....

....

....

Weight

....

Length

....

Head circumference

....

Time spent playing on the floor

....

....

Crying periods

....

....

....

Best way to calm your baby boy

....

....

....

Changes

....

....

....

New teeth

....

....

Teething symptoms and remedies

....

....

....

Baby at 10 months

New sounds

....

....

New firsts

....

....

....

....

Your baby boy's temperament

....

....

....

Nicknames

....

....

Description of a typical day

....

....

....

Preferred activities

....

....

....

Photo caption

....

....

....

Date photo taken

....

Preferred foods

....

....

....

12 Months Old

Usually woke for the day at

....

....

Went to bed for the day at

....

....

Daytime sleep routine

....

....

Daytime feeding routine

....

....

Night-time sleeping and feeding routine

....

....

....

Photo caption

....

....

....

Date photo taken

....

....

Baby at 12 months

Weight

....

Length

....

Head circumference

....

Time spent playing on the floor

....

....

Crying periods

....

....

Best way to calm your baby boy

....

....

....

Changes

....

....

New teeth

....

....

....

Teething symptoms and remedies

....

....

....

New sounds

....

....

New firsts

....

....

Your baby boy's temperament

....

....

Nicknames

....

....

Description of a typical day

....

....

....

Preferred activities

....

....

....

Preferred foods

....

....

Your Baby Boy's Firsts

First smile

July 2016 - Less than a month old!

First gripped rattle

First laughed

First tooth

First haircut

Clever baby boy

First slept through the night

Photo caption

First said 'Mama'

Date photo taken

40

First said 'Dada'

....

....

First waved goodbye

....

....

First rolled

....

....

First sat

....

....

First crawled

....

....

First stood

....

....

First walked

....

....

First babysitter

....

....

I had a little nut tree,
Nothing would it bear,
But a silver nutmeg,
And a golden pear.

First Christmas

Christmas Eve
Where the day was spent

....
....
....
....
....

Who was there

....
....
....
....

Baby's outfit

....

Description of your baby boy's
first Christmas Eve

....
....

Christmas Day
Where the day was spent

....
....
....
....
....

Who was there

....
....
....
....

Your present to your baby boy

....
....
....
....
....

Other presents

....
....
....
....

42

Present your baby boy loved the most

....

....

First Christmas meal

....

....

....

Baby boy's outfit

....

....

....

Description of the Christmas tree

....

....

....

Description of your baby boy's first Christmas Day

....

....

....

*O*n the first day of Christmas
My true love gave to me
A partridge in a pear tree.

First Christmas

Photo caption

....

....

Date photo taken

....

....

First Birthday

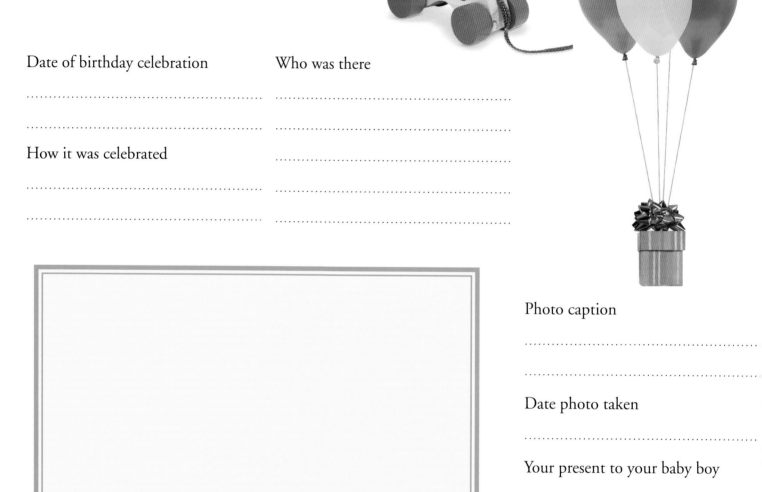

Date of birthday celebration

....

....

How it was celebrated

....

....

Who was there

....

....

....

....

Photo caption

....

....

Date photo taken

....

Your present to your baby boy

....

....

....

....

First birthday

Other presents

....

....

....

....

....

Baby boy's outfit

....

....

....

How baby behaved

....

....

....

Baby boy's reaction when
'Happy Birthday' sung

....

....

....

....

....

Description of cake

....

....

....

Description of birthday celebration

....

....

....

....

....

....

Memorable moments

....

....

....

....

....

....

....

....

Going on Holiday

First Holiday
People who went

....

....

....

....

How long away

....

....

....

Getting there details

....

....

....

Accommodation details

....

....

....

Toys and books taken

....

....

....

Baby boy's holiday routine

....

....

New experiences

....

....

....

Holiday highlights

....

....

Memorable moments

....

....

....

....

Other Holidays
Holiday highlights

....

....

....

Memorable moments

....

....

....

On holiday

Photo caption

....

....

Date photo taken

....

The grand old Duke of York,

He had ten thousand men,

He marched them up to the top of the hill,

Then he marched them down again!

And when they were up they were up,

And when they were down they were down,

And when they were only halfway up,

They were neither up nor down.

Looking Back

Baby Boy's First Year

Greatest pleasure

....
....
....
....
....
....
....

Greatest challenge

Sleep schedule for mom +
Dad.
Christian only wants to
be held at all times.
....
....
....

Siblings' early reaction to baby

Erik was 13 when he
was told about you.
He was very excited
to finally have a brother
....
....
....

Siblings' relationship
with baby now

....
....
....
....
....

Your baby boy's personality

6 weeks old- curious,
inquizative + happy
....
....
....
....
....

Thoughts on being a family

Never happier :)
....
....
....
....